The
Green Carnivore

by Frederick Miller
illustrated by Richard Guerriero

Copyright © by Harcourt, Inc.

All rights reserved. No part of this publication may be reproduced or transmitted in any form or by any means, electronic or mechanical, including photocopy, recording, or any information storage and retrieval system, without permission in writing from the publisher.

Requests for permission to make copies of any part of the work should be mailed to the following address: School Permissions, Harcourt, Inc., 6277 Sea Harbor Drive, Orlando, Florida 32887-6777.

HARCOURT and the Harcourt Logo are trademarks of Harcourt, Inc.

Printed in the United States of America

ISBN 0-15-319511-8

Ordering Options
ISBN 0-15-316988-5 (Grade 4 Collection)
ISBN 0-15-319700-5 (package of 5)

2 3 4 5 6 7 8 9 10 179 2003 2002 2001 2000

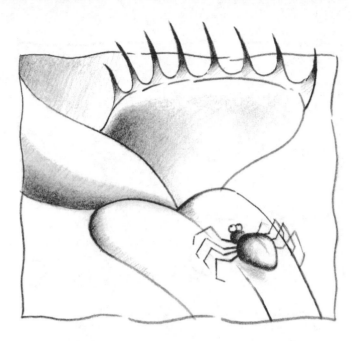

Carnivorous plants are those that eat meat.
The way they eat bugs is awfully neat.
They're clever, so remember, please,
They've got some tricks right up their sleeves.

Little spider, won't you please watch out?
I do know what I'm talking about.
These plants are green,
These plants are mean.
Don't be fooled by a leaf that's part red,
Just stay away, or you'll wind up dead.

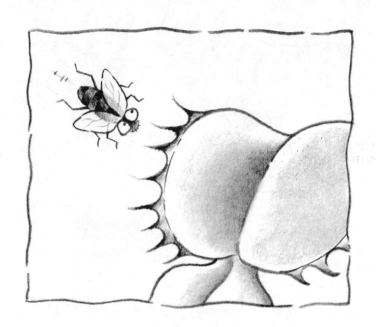

The Venus flytrap is carnivorous.
From this plant the fly said, "Deliver us."
Once you land on its leaf, it is too late—
Its jaws will snap shut, and you won't escape.

Little fly, won't you please watch out?
I do know what I'm talking about.
These plants are green,
These plants are mean.
Don't be fooled by their sweet-smelling nectar,
Just stay away, or you'll wind up dead, dear.

Flytraps live in the boggiest places,
But look like they come from outer spaces.
Watch the spider crawl onto the leaf,
Touch two trigger hairs, and come to grief.

Little spider, won't you please watch out?
I do know what I'm talking about.
These plants are green,
These plants are mean.
If you're small you can, with enough resolve,
Slip out of the trap before you dissolve.

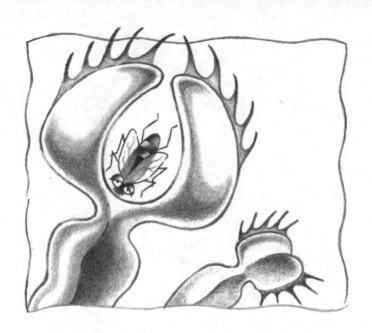

If, fly, you should accidentally land,
Before things get even more out of hand,
Please crawl away. Just crawl away.
And live to see another day.

Little fly, won't you please watch out?
I do know what I'm talking about.
These plants are green,
These plants are mean.
Ol' Venus will surely dissolve you for lunch,
If her chemicals don't dissolve you at brunch.

In the boggiest corners of North Carolina,
For Ol' Venus flytrap nothing could be finer.
Far from farmers who may use fertilizer,
No fertilizer here to shock or surprise her.

Little spider, won't you please watch out?
I do know what I'm talking about.
These plants are green,
These plants are mean.
Ol' Venus will digest you in eight to ten days,
If you ever fall victim to her evil ways.

One day a wasp smelled something so sweet,
It swooped down fast, landing flat on its feet.
But sensing trouble, it cleared the trapdoor,
Before Ol' Venus could clamp shut its jaw.

Little wasp, won't you please watch out?
I do know what I'm talking about.
These plants are green,
These plants are mean.
You were lucky this time, you'll surely agree.
Don't do this again, if you want to stay free.

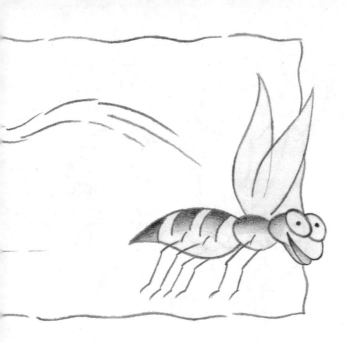

Here's good news for flies and wasps and bees—
Ol' Venus eats her meals by threes.
A flytrap's leaf that's eaten three meals,
Withers and dies without any squeals.

Little wasp, won't you please watch out?
I do know what I'm talking about.
These plants are green,
These plants are mean.
Ol' Venus, the wasp got away from you.
I do want to see more escape, I do.

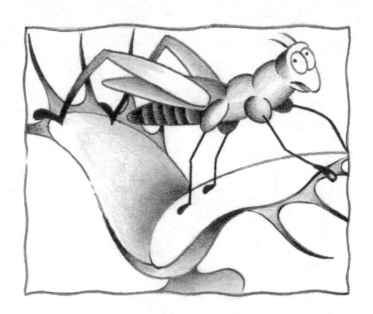

A grasshopper's a creature of special renown.
It leaps over flytraps in one single bound.
Now he's fallen into Ol' Venus's lap,
Will he be strong enough to spring the trap?

O grasshopper, won't you please watch out?
I do know what I'm talking about.
These plants are green,
These plants are mean.
Though you've accidentally gotten trapped,
The bars of your cage I see you've snapped.

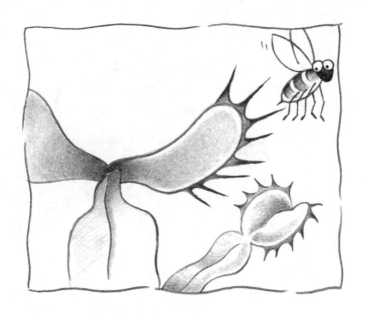

What is that I see, hunting for treasure?
It's you, honeybee, buzzing for pleasure.
If Venus is lucky, you will be undone.
I'm hoping a victim you will not become.

Little bee, won't you please watch out?
I do know what I'm talking about.
These plants are green,
These plants are mean.
Ol' Venus, you think you can trick this bee,
But the bee's too smart for you, I can see.

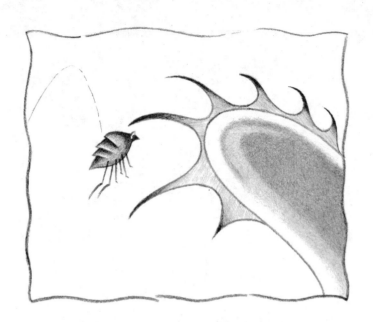

As for dinner, Ol' Venus still goes without,
Yet I cannot see any creature about.
Wait, what is that tiny speck in the air?
A flea, heading for Venus's trigger hair.

Little flea, won't you please watch out?
I do know what I'm talking about.
These plants are green,
These plants are mean.
Ol' Venus just loves little guys like you.
With chemicals she'll prepare a flea stew.

Listen, Ol' Venus, I'll bet you just wish,
You could get up and hunt for a tasty dish,
Like all the creatures who fly through the air.
I guess you might think that life isn't fair.

Little bugs, won't you please watch out?
I do know what I'm talking about.
These plants are green,
These plants are mean.
Ol' Venus sits there, plotting and scheming,
Hoping you'll visit so she can stop dreaming.

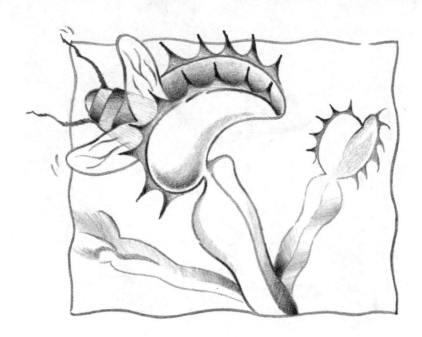

Poor Ol' Venus flytrap is getting real hungry.
The way things are going is no longer funny.
Wait a minute—here's a fly I haven't seen yet.
Looks like dinner is near for Ol' Venus, I'll bet.

Little fly, won't you please watch out?
I do know what I'm talking about.
These plants are green,
These plants are mean.
I tried to warn you, and now it's too late,
But even flytraps must eat—and that's fate!

True or False

What do you remember about the Venus flytrap? Number a sheet of paper from 1 to 9. Write *T* if the statement is true. Write *F* if the statement is false. (Answers are on the back of this page.)

___1. Carnivorous plants are those that eat meat.

___2. The red part of the Venus flytrap's leaf is the safest part for an insect.

___3. The Venus flytrap is not carnivorous.

___4. Insects are attracted to the Venus flytrap by the sweet smell of its nectar.

___5. Venus flytraps can be found in swamps in North Carolina.

___6. Trigger hairs on the leaves of the Venus flytrap can cause the plant to wilt.

___7. The Venus flytrap uses chemicals to dissolve insects that are trapped in its leaves.

___8. Venus flytraps respond well to fertilizer.

___9. Grasshoppers are strong enough so that they can sometimes break out of the Venus flytrap's "cage."

School-Home Connection Have your child read the poem aloud to you. Then, to emphasize the rhyming words in this poem, say these words out loud: *meat, leaf, lunch, days, feet, trapped.* Have your child say aloud the word in the poem, or another word, that rhymes with each word.

Answers:
Statements 1, 4, 5, 7, and 9 are true; statements 2, 3, 6, and 8 are false.